Flute Exam Pieces

ABRSM Grade 4

Selected from the 2014–2017 syllabus

Name

Date of exam

Contents

Footnotes: Anthony Burton and Rachel Brown (RB)

Other pieces for Grade 4

First published in 2013 by ABRSM (Publishing) Ltd, a wholly owned subsidiary of ABRSM, 24 Portland Place, London W1B 1LU, United Kingdom © 2013 by The Associated Board of the Royal Schools of Music

Music origination by Andrew Jones Cover by Kate Benjamin & Andy Potts Printed in England by Caligraving Ltd, Thetford, Norfolk

MIX
Paper from responsible sources
FSC™ C109619

A:1

Sonata in G

Arranged by Giovanni Gatti
and Angela Sogni

Domenico Cimarosa
(1749–1801)

Domenico Cimarosa, born near Naples in southern Italy, was one of the most famous composers of comic operas of his time, although his operas have since been eclipsed by those of his younger contemporary Mozart. He also composed sacred music, a few orchestral works, and more than 80 sonatas for keyboard (harpsichord or piano). Like the sonatas of Domenico Scarlatti earlier in the 18th century, these are each in a single movement, though their layout in some manuscripts suggests that they might have been combined to make longer works. This is an arrangement of one such sonata movement. A number of inconsistencies in dynamics, articulation and breath marks have been corrected here without comment.

Allegro

Fourth movement from Sonata No. 1 in D minor

Edited by and continuo
realization by Rachel Brown

Francesco Mancini
(1672–1737)

The Neapolitan composer Francesco Mancini was highly prolific, with several operas, oratorios and secular cantatas to his name, yet today he is chiefly remembered for his recorder sonatas, from which this lively movement is taken. Ever anxious to curry political favour, Mancini dedicated these sonatas, published in London, to the Hon'ble John Fleetwood, Consul General for the King of Naples. Suspensions and syncopations should be clearly detached from preceding notes. Bars 14–15 (and similar cadential approaches at bars 23–24 and 43–44) introduce the cross rhythms of a hemiola, falling effectively into one 3/4 time bar (as opposed to two bars in 3/8 time). Repeating the last phrase softly (as here from the upbeat to bar 60) was a popular effect used by the Italian master Corelli. The dynamics, apart from the *piano* marking in bar 59, are editorial, as are the slurs in bars 23 and 50, all staccato marks, and the trills in bars 24, 26, 44, 58 and 66. RB

Source: *XII Solos for a violin or flute* (London, 1724)

Menuetto and Trio

Second movement from Flute Quartet in A, K. 298

Arranged by Heinz Stolba

W. A. Mozart
(1756–91)

Menuetto da capo

The great Austrian composer Wolfgang Amadeus Mozart wrote three or four flute quartets – that is, quartets for flute, violin, viola and cello. Counting them as 'three or four' is because one of them, although it has Mozart's name on it and includes some music by him, may not be by him at all. But there is no doubt about the authenticity of the quartet numbered 298 in Köchel's catalogue, because a manuscript has survived in Mozart's handwriting. It was probably written in about 1786 for music-making in the household of the Jacquin family, friends of Mozart's in Vienna. The piece is based largely on melodies by other composers. This minuet has as its main theme a version of an old French tune, *Il a des bottes, des bottes, Bastien* ('He has boots, boots, does Bastien') – though nobody has yet found a source for the melody of the central trio section. In this version, the flute part is unchanged, while the three string parts are arranged for the piano.

Lonely and Blue

from *Hartbeat*

B:1

Paul Hart
(born 1954)

Paul Hart studied piano, violin and composition at the Royal College of Music in London, but left to play bass, piano and violin for the jazz singer Cleo Laine and her saxophonist husband John Dankworth. He has composed works for orchestra, jazz orchestra and wind band, and has written concertos for the guitarist John Williams and the percussionist Evelyn Glennie, as well as music for several television series. 'Lonely and Blue' comes from a collection of pieces for flute and piano, published in 2011, called *Hartbeat*. As indicated, it should be played with swung quavers, including rests and tied notes. The composer suggests that its mood is one of defiance: 'You are standing up to those around you despite your inner feelings.'

Romance

Arthur Honegger
(1892–1955)

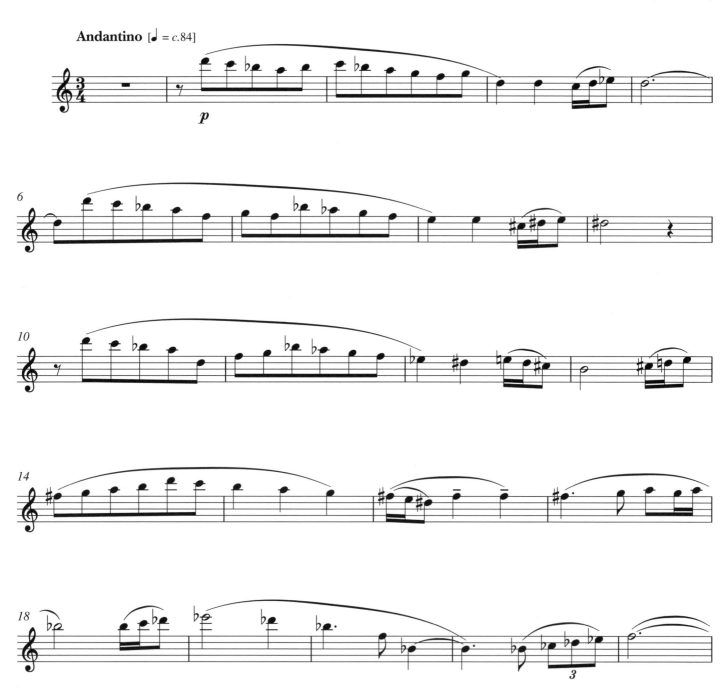

Arthur Honegger was born to Swiss parents in France, and lived for most of his life in Paris. In the years around 1920, he was identified as a member of the group called 'Les Six', who wrote deliberately cheerful and carefree music as a reaction to the stresses of the First World War. But his mature music is generally more serious in feeling. Honegger composed operas, ballets, film scores, concert works for orchestra – including a famous musical description of a steam train journey, *Pacific 231* – and songs, as well as a great deal of instrumental music. He wrote this *Romance* for flute and piano in 1952 or '53, towards the end of his life (it may well have been his last composition), for inclusion in one of a series of albums of short pieces called *Les Contemporains écrivent pour les instruments à vent* ('Contemporary composers write for wind instruments'), compiled and edited by the bassoonist Fernand Oubradous. The flowing flute line is accompanied by harmonies which are typical of Honegger's free use of dissonance.

B:3

Gavotte

from *The Gondoliers*

Arranged by Ian Denley

W. S. Gilbert (1836–1911) and
Arthur Sullivan (1842–1900)

Tempo di Gavotte – Allegretto ♩ = *c.*60

mf with as full a sound as possible

Sir Arthur Sullivan formed a famous partnership with the writer William Schwenk Gilbert to produce a popular series of comic operas, known as the 'Savoy operas' after the London theatre in which they were first presented. One of the last of the series is *The Gondoliers*, first performed in 1889. This is set partly in Venice, the home of the gondoliers (or boatmen) of the title, and partly in the imaginary kingdom of Barataria. In this number, originally for soloists, chorus and orchestra, the Spanish Duke of Plaza-Toro instructs the gondoliers in how to behave at court, including the dancing of the gavotte. This is a dance of French origin, popular in operas and concert music in the 17th and 18th centuries, in a stately duple metre and always beginning halfway through the bar.

The Wind in the Withies

No. 3 from *Somerset Scenes for Solo Flute*

Colin Cowles
(born 1940)

Colin Cowles grew up playing woodwind instruments, but studied piano, organ and composition at Trinity College of Music in London. He taught at schools in the south-east of England before becoming a peripatetic woodwind teacher and examiner – which allowed him more time to compose both large-scale works and educational music. Since 1991 he has lived on the Somerset Levels, a wetland area in south-west England. He describes his *Somerset Scenes for Solo Flute* as 'five contemporary folk-tunes' – meaning original pieces in folk style. The third of them is called 'The Wind in the Withies' which is a variation on the title of Kenneth Grahame's classic children's novel, *The Wind in the Willows*, as 'withies' means willow branches.

Study in E minor

No. 19 from *30 Études faciles et progressives*

C:2

Giuseppe Gariboldi
(1833–1905)

Études faciles et progressives Easy and Progressive Studies

Giuseppe Gariboldi was an Italian-born flautist who established himself in Paris and became a leading figure in French musical life. He published over 300 works, including solos, duets and studies for the flute. This Study is not only a test of finger and breath control, the latter especially in its rising octaves, but also an exercise in precise articulation. The source contains some inconsistencies in dynamics which have been corrected here without comment.

Source: *Études faciles et progressives pour la flûte* (London: Augener & Co., 1892)

Allegretto

No. 30 from *Easy Jazz Singles*

Russell Stokes
(born 1958)

Russell Stokes, born in London, is a flautist, pianist, teacher and composer with a particular interest in jazz styles. He says that his *Jazz Singles* series of studies 'introduces students to technical challenges within a popular and contemporary idiom'. In this piece, written in a 'jazz swing style', he suggests that 'the tongue should not be used too firmly, but should have an almost lazy feel'.